THE

HA-HA

HEE-HEE

HO-HO

JOKE BOOK

© 1985 GRANDREAMS LIMITED

Published by
GRANDREAMS LIMITED
Jadwin House, 205/211 Kentish Town Road,
London NW5.

Printed in Hungary

JB1-2   ISBN 0 86227 298 X

CONTENTS

IT MUST BE TROUBLE!

When things go wrong, what can you always count on?
Your fingers.

Why was the musician arrested?
He got into treble (trouble).

Why were screams coming from the kitchen?
The cook was beating the eggs.

Is it dangerous to swim on a full stomach?
Yes. It is better to swim in water.

Why is a banana peel on the pavement like music?
Because if you don't C sharp you'll B flat.

If you plug your electric blanket into the toaster, what happens?
You pop up all night.

For how long a period of time did Cain hate his brother?
As long as he was Abel (able).

What kind of spy hangs around department stores?
A counterspy.

What happened when the man sat on a pin?
Nothing. It was a safety pin.

How can you avoid falling hair?
Get out of the way.

Why did the spy speak in a whisper?
Because he was on a hush-hush mission.

What should a girl wear when she wants to end a fight?
Makeup.

Why is an eye like a man being flogged?
Because it's under the lash.

When do public speakers steal lumber?
When they take the floor.

What do you call a baby whale that cries?
A little blubber.

What did the delicatessen sell after it burned down?
Smoked meats.

What criminals can you find in a shoe store?
A pair of sneakers.

What diploma do criminals get?
The third degree.

When is a clock nervous?
When it is all wound up.

Why do people beat their clocks?
To kill time.

Who were the first gamblers?
Adam and Eve. They had a paradise (pair of dice).

Spell mousetrap with three letters.
C-A-T.

Why wasn't the girl afraid of the shark?
Because it was a man-eating shark.

Why is a dictionary dangerous?
Because it has "dynamite" in it.

A policeman saw a truck driver going the wrong way
down a one-way street, but didn't give him a ticket. Why
not?
The truck driver was walking.

If you were walking in a jungle and saw a lion, what time
would it be?
Time to run.

Why shouldn't you grab a tiger by his tail?
It may only be his tail, but it could be your end.

If an African lion fought an African tiger, who would win?
Neither. There are no tigers in Africa.

Why does a dog chasing a rabbit resemble a bald-headed
man?
He makes a little hare (hair) go a long way.

What would you have if your car's motor was in flames?
A fire engine.

What did the rug say to the floor?
"I've got you covered."

What did the picture say to the wall?
"I've been framed."

Where is the best place to hide a lawyer?
In a brief case.

When did the criminal get smart?
When the judge threw the book at him.

Why is your heart like a policeman?
Because it follows a regular beat.

Why can't you keep secrets in a bank?
Because of all the tellers.

Can you spell jealousy with two letters?
NV (envy).

What did the cork say to the bottle?
"If you don't behave yourself, I'll plug you."

What did one cucumber say to the other cucumber?
"If you had kept your big mouth shut, we wouldn't be in this pickle."

Why did the hens refuse to lay any more eggs?
Because they were tired of working for chicken feed.

What would happen if black widow spiders were as big as horses?
If one bit you, you could ride it to the hospital.

What Indian goes to court?
A Sioux (sue) Indian.

What kind of clothes do lawyers wear?
Lawsuits.

What kind of soldier doesn't need bullets?
   A soldier who is always shooting his mouth off.

When is an army totally destroyed?
   When it is in quarters.

What is in the army and is corny?
   A colonel (kernel).

Why did the kid punch the bed?
   His mother told him to hit the hay.

Why did the cowboy get a hot seat?
   Because he rode the range.

Why was the lobster arrested?
   Because he was always pinching things.

What do animals read in zoos?
Gnus papers!

Why did the sheriff arrest the tree?
   Because its leaves rustled.

How did the chimpanzee escape from his cage?
   He used a monkey wrench.

What bird always runs from a fight?
   A canary, because it is yellow.

Why are farmers cruel?
   Because they pull corn by the ears.

What did the kangaroo say when her baby was missing?
   "Help! My pocket's been picked."

What do you call a man when a Marine sits on him?
A submarine.

Why is it confusing when a dog growls and wags his tail at the same time?
It's hard to know which end to believe.

What is a very hair-raising experience?
Visiting a rabbit farm.

What letter should you avoid?
The letter A because it makes men mean.

How can you jump off a 50-foot ladder without getting hurt?
Jump off the bottom rung.

If five boys beat up one boy, what time would it be?
Five to one.

If you were surrounded by 10 lions, 4 tigers, 3 grizzly bears and 4 leopards, how could you escape?
Wait until the merry-go-round stops and get off.

What is big and white and is found in Florida?
A lost polar bear.

Why couldn't the clock be kept in gaol?
Because time was always running out.

What kind of robbery is not dangerous?
A safe robbery.

What kind of Indians does Dracula like?
Full-blooded ones.

Why did the outlaw carry a bottle of glue when he went to rob the stagecoach?
He wanted to stick up the passenger.

People's houses have rooms. What does Dracula's house have?
Glooms.

Why did the chicken run away from home?
Because she was tired of being cooped up.

How do you spell a hated opponent with three letters?
NME (enemy).

Why did the dog run away from home?
Doggone if I know!

Why was the sheep arrested on the motorway?
Because it made an ewe turn!

Why is a sinking ship like a person in jail?
Because it needs bailing out.

Why did the robber take a bath?
So he could make a clean getaway.

What kind of puzzle makes people angry?
A crossword puzzle.

How can you tell when a mummy is angry?
When he flips his lid.

What happened when the chimney got angry?
It blew its stack.

Why is the ocean angry?
Because it has been crossed so many times.

Why is a thief like a thermometer on a hot day?
Because they are both up to something.

What is the difference between a thief and a church bell?
One steals from the people, the other peals from the steeple.

Why does Father Time wear bandages?
Because day breaks and night falls.

What did one skunk say to the other skunk when they were cornered?
"Let us spray."

What weapon is most feared by knights?
A can opener.

What is a rifle with three barrels?
A trifle.

When do ghosts have to stop scaring people?
When they lose their haunting (hunting) licences.

Why is it hard to steal pigs?
Because pigs are squealers.

What animal breaks the law?
A cheetah.

What animal has a chip on its shoulder?
A chipmunk.

What is a skunk's best defence against enemies?
Instinct.

If you cross a lion and a mouse, what will you have?
  A mighty mouse.

How can you come face-to-face with a hungry, angry lion, dare him to fight, and still be unafraid?
  Walk calmly to the next cage.

Why was the insect kicked out of the forest?
  Because it was a litterbug.

What did one clock say to the other clock when it was frightened?
  "Don't be alarmed."

What did the coward say to the stamp?
  "I bet I can lick you."

Why don't polar bears eat penguins?
They can't get the silver paper off!

What did the leopard say when he swallowed the man?
  "That hit the spot!"

What was the most dangerous time for knights?
  Nightfall (knight fall).

What would you get if Batman and Robin were run over by a herd of stampeding elephants?
  Flatman and Ribbon.

How does an octopus go to war?
  Armed.

Why is law like the ocean?
  Because most trouble is caused by the breakers.

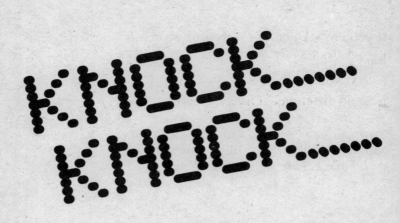

KNOCK———
KNOCK———

Who's there?
Louisiana.
Louisiana who?
Louisiana boy friend broke up.

Who's there?
Luke.
Luke who?
Luke before you leap.

Who's there?
Lyndon.
Lyndon who?
Lyndon ear and I'll tell you.

Who's there?
Major.
Major who?
Major answer this knock-knock joke.

Who's there?
Mara.
Mara who?
"Mara, Mara, on the wall . . ."

Who's there?
Marcella.
Marcella who?
Marcella is full of water and I'm drowning. Help!

Who's there?
Marion.
Marion who?
Marion haste, repent at leisure.

Who's there?
Max.
  Max who?
Max no difference. Open the door.

          Who's there?
          Maybelle.
            Maybelle who?
          Maybelle (my bell) doesn't ring, either.

Who's there?
Meg.
  Meg who?
Meg up your mind.

          Who's there?
          Midas.
            Midas who?
          Midas well relax. I'm not going any place.

Who's there?
Minerva.
  Minerva who?
Minerva-s wreck from all these questions.

          Who's there?
          Miniature.
            Miniature who?
          Miniature open your mouth, you put your foot in it.

Who's there?
Minneapolis.
  Minneapolis who?
Minneapolis each day keep many doctors away.

          Who's there?
          Minnie.
            Minnie who?
          No, not Minnie-who—Minnehaha.

Who's there?
Mitzi.
  Mitzi who?
Mitzi door shut, you'll never find out.

IT'S A MAD WORLD!

How does a witch tell time?
With a witch watch.

Who drives away all of his customers?
A taxicab driver.

What driver doesn't have a licence?
A screwdriver.

What do you call a high-priced barber shop?
A clip joint.

If you cross a telephone and a pair of scissors, what do you get?
Snippy answers.

If you cross a telephone and a lobster, what will you get?
Snappy talk.

Who is bigger, Mrs. Bigger or her baby?
Her baby is a little Bigger.

What is purple and 5,000 miles long?
The Grape Wall of China.

What is green, has two legs and a trunk?
A seasick tourist.

What do you call an Indian woman who complains a lot?
A squaw-ker.

Why do we dress baby girls in pink and baby boys in blue?
Because they can't dress themselves.

What is the difference between an umbrella and a person who never stops talking?
The umbrella can be shut up.

Why do people buy things with their credit cards?
They get a charge out of it.

What is the most important use for cowhide?
It helps keep the cow together.

Who was the first to have a mobile home?
A turtle.

What kind of ears do trains have?
Engineers (engine ears).

Why shouldn't you tell secrets when a clock is around?
Because time will tell.

What is a drill team?
A group of dentists who work together.

Where can you always find health, wealth and happiness?
In the dictionary.

What is an astronaut's favourite meal?
Launch.

What can you serve but never eat?
A tennis ball.

What kind of tables do people eat?
Vegetables.

What is a wisecrack?
> *An educated hole in the wall.*

What kind of fence goes on strike?
> *A picket fence.*

A man who worked in the butcher shop was 6 feet tall, had red hair and wore size 11 shoes. What did he weigh?
> *Meat.*

What is lemonade?
> *When you help an old lemon cross the street.*

What socks do you find in your back yard?
> *Garden hose.*

What do you call a camel with three humps?
Humphrey!

What has a head, can't think, but drives?
> *A hammer.*

What kind of test does a vampire take in school?
> *A blood test.*

What is the best way to prevent milk from turning sour?
> *Leave it in the cow.*

How does a coffee pot feel when it is hot?
> *Perky.*

What is blue, green, yellow, purple, brown, black, and grey?
> *A box of crayons.*

How can you make any watch a stopwatch?
> *Don't wind it.*

How can you make money fast?
Glue it to the floor.

How can you make a soup rich?
Add 14 carrots (carats) to it.

Why did the hippie put his money in the refrigerator?
He liked cold cash.

What happened when the man asked the salesman for a good belt?
"O.K., you asked for it," the salesman said as he gave him a good belt.

How does a pair of trousers feel when it is ironed?
Depressed.

Why was the shoe unhappy?
Because his father was a loafer and his mother a sneaker.

What did one skunk say to the other?
"So do you!"

What did one pig say to the other pig?
"Let's be pen pals."

What do you do with dogs when you go shopping?
Leave them in the car bark (park).

What is a dog catcher?
A Spot remover.

What did the two vampires do from midnight to 12:10?
They took a coffin (coffee) break.

What did the fly say when he landed on the book?
"I think I've read this story before."

Why can't a bicycle stand up by itself?
Because it is two-tyred (too tired).

What is 10+5 minus 15? What is 3+6 minus 9? What is 17+3 minus 20?
All that work for nothing.

If Washington's wife went to Washington while Washington's washwoman washed Washington's woollies, how many W's are there in all?
None. There are no W's in "all."

How do you make a Venetian blind?
Stick a finger in his eye.

Where did the three little kittens find their mittens?
In the Yellow Pages.

What is the difference between twice twenty-two and twice two and twenty?
One is 44, the other is 24.

Why do they say George Washington was an orphan?
He was the foundling father of his country.

Why do they say George Washington couldn't swim?
He was the foundering father of his country.

Why was George Washington like a fish?
He was the flounder of his country.

When does a bed grow longer?
At night, because two feet are added to it.

Why do lions eat raw meat?
Because they don't know how to cook.

What kind of car do werewolves buy?
A Wolfswagen.

What would you call a grandfather clock?
An old timer.

How many letters are there in the alphabet?
Eleven. T-H-E A-L-P-H-A-B-E-T.

Did Adam and Eve ever have a date?
No, they had an apple.

What kind of nut has no shell?
A doughnut.

What is a stupid flower?
A blooming idiot.

What can you do with old bowling balls?
Give them to elephants to shoot marbles.

Why couldn't Humpty Dumpty be put together again?
Because he wasn't everything he was cracked up to be.

In a certain city there is a corner with four shops. One is a baker's, one a sweet shop, one a chemist, and one a book shop. Outside the chemist is a policeman. Why is the policeman called Oscar?
Because that is his name.

Dogs have fleas. What do sheep have?
Fleece.

What would happen if you swallowed a frog?
You might croak.

Where do trees keep their money?
In branch banks.

Where do Eskimos keep their money?
In snowbanks.

Where do fish keep their money?
In river banks.

Where do vampires keep their money?
In blood banks.

"Where did Abraham Lincoln live?"
"I have his Gettysburg Address right here!"

What do snake charmers do in the rain?
Turn on their windscreen vipers!

If cheese comes on top of a hamburger, what comes after cheese?
A mouse.

Where do mummies swim?
In the Dead Sea.

What is the best way to eat spaghetti?
First, open your mouth.

The alphabet goes from A to Z. What goes from Z to A?
Zebra.

What is the best way to cure someone who walks in his sleep?
Put tacks on the floor.

What has a head but no brain?
A cabbage.

What is a grasshopper?
An insect on a pogo stick.

What did one mountain say to the other mountain after an earthquake?
"It's not my fault."

What did the boy centipede say to the girl centipede?
"You sure have a nice pair of legs, pair of legs, pair of legs . . ."

What did the little light bulb say to its mother?
"I wuv you watts and watts."

What is the best way to make trousers last?
Make the jacket first.

What makes more noise than a squealing pig?
Two squealing pigs.

What happened when Abel died?
He became unable.

Why do wallets make so much noise?
Because money talks.

What happens to a refrigerator when you pull its plug?
It loses its cool.

What room can you bounce around in?
A ballroom.

What is a tongue twister?
When your tang gets all tongueled up.

When should you charge a new battery?
When you can't pay cash.

How many skunks does it take to make a big skunk?
A phew (few).

Why did the invisible man look in the mirror?
To see if he still wasn't there.

What does an invisible baby drink?
Evaporated milk.

What runs around all day and then lies under the bed with its tongue hanging out?
Your shoe.

What is a briefcase?
A short law suit.

When does an Irish potato change nationality?
When it is French fried.

To whom did Paul Revere give his handkerchief?
To the town crier.

What did King Kong say when he saw the Statue of Liberty?
"Are you my mother?"

What is bacteria?
The rear entrance of a cafeteria.

What is a bulldozer?
Someone who sleeps while a politician is making a speech.

Where do ghosts go for fresh air?
To the sea ghost (coast).

How can you tell when there is an elephant in your sandwich?
When it is too heavy to lift.

How do you fit five elephants into a Volkswagen?
Two in the front, two in the back and one in the glove compartment.

What fish did the knights eat?
Swordfish.

How would you address a gorilla?
Politely.

What fish do pelicans eat?
Anything that fits the bill.

When is a bicycle not a bicycle?
When it turns into a driveway.

What is red and goes up and down?
A tomato in an elevator.

What lottery did the broom win?
The sweepstakes.

What keys won't open doors?
Don-keys, mon-keys, tur-keys.

Who's there?
Nadya.
Nadya who?
Nadya head if you understand what I'm saying.

Who's there?
Marmalade.
Marmalade who?
"Marmalade me," said the little chicken.

Who's there?
Matthew.
Matthew who?
Matthew is pinthing my foot.

Who's there?
Maura.
Maura who?
The Maura the merrier.

Who's there?
Monkey.
Monkey who?
Monkey won't fit, that's why I knocked.

Who's there?
Moose.
Moose who?
Moose you be so nosy?

Who's there?
Myth.
Myth who?
Myth you, too.

Who's there?
Nana.
  Nana who?
Nana your business.

                              Who's there?
                          Nettie.
                              Nettie who?
                          Nettie as a fruitcake.

Who's there?
Noah.
  Noah who?
"Noahbody knows the trouble I've seen . . ."

Who's there?
Norma Lee.
  Norma Lee who?
Norma Lee I don't go around knocking on doors, but I
have this wonderful set of encyclopaedias . . .

Who's there?
Nuisance.
  Nuisance who?
What's nuisance yesterday?

                              Who's there?
                          Nurse.
                              Nurse who?
                          Nurse sense in talking to you.

Who's there?
Obadiah. (Pronounced O-bad-eye-ah)
  Obadiah who?
Obadiah (oh, I'm dying) from dis cold.

                              Who's there?
                          Ocelot.
                              Ocelot who?
                          Ocelot of questions, don't you?

Who's there?
Odette
  Odette who?
Odette's a bad sign.

Who's there?
Ohio.
Ohio who?
Ohio Silver!

Who's there?
Olaf.
Olaf who?
Olaf you.

Who's there?
Oldest son.
Oldest son who?
"Oldest son shines bright on my old Kentucky
home . . ."

Who's there?
Olive.
Olive who?
Olive none of your lip.

Who's there?
Oliver.
Oliver who?
Oliver troubles are over.

Who's there?
Olivia.
Olivia who?
Olivia (I live here) but I forgot my key.

Who's there?
Ollie.
·Ollie who?
Ollie time you say that, I wish you'd cut it out.

Who's there?
Omar.
Omar who?
Omar goodness gracious! Wrong door!

Who's there?
Ooze.
Ooze who?
Ooze in charge around here?

Who's there?
Odessa.
Odessa who?
Odessa hot one!

Who's there?
Oscar.
Oscar who?
Oscar silly question, get a silly answer.

Who's there?
O'Shea.
O'Shea who?
O'Shea, that's a shad shtory.

Who's there?
Oslo.
Oslo who?
Oslo down. Where's the fire?

Who's there?
Oswego.
Oswego who?
"Oswego marching, marching home . . ."

Who's there?
Owen.
Owen who?
"Owen the saints go marching in . . ."

Who's there?
Owl.
Owl who?
Owl aboard!

Who's there?
Ozzie.
Ozzie who?
Ozzie you later.

Who's there?
Passion.
Passion who?
Passion by and thought I'd say "Hello."

WINNERS & LOSERS

How do chickens start a race?
From scratch.

What is a fast duck?
A quick quack.

Why did the orange stop in the middle of the road?
It ran out of juice.

A lemon and an orange were on a high diving board. The orange jumped off. Why didn't the lemon?
Because it was yellow.

Why did they throw the elephants out of the swimming pool?
Because they couldn't hold their trunks up.

Why shouldn't you tell a joke while you are ice skating?
Because the ice might crack up.

Why don't sheep have much money?
Because they're always getting fleeced.

Why did the kangaroo mother scold her child?
For eating crackers in bed.

Why wasn't the elephant allowed on the aeroplane?
Because his trunk was too big to fit under the seat.

What kind of party do prisoners in jail like most of all?
A going-away party.

When do clocks die?
When their time is up.

What game can be dangerous to your mental health?
Marbles, if you lose them.

What stars go to jail?
Shooting stars.

What did the bee say to the rose?
"Hi, Bud!"

What did the rose answer?
"Buzz off!"

What did the blackbird say to the scarecrow?
"I can beat the stuffing out of you!"

What did one grape say to the other grape?
"If it wasn't for you, we wouldn't be in this jam."

Why are jackasses good football players?
Because when they kick they seldom miss.

What is the difference between an ice cream cone and a bully?
You lick one, the other licks you.

When it rains cats and dogs, what do you step into?
Poodles.

What did the frankfurter say when the dog bit him?
"It's a dog-eat-dog world."

How is a ghost child taught to count to ten?
One, boo, three, four, five, six, seven, hate, nine, frighten.

What did the yacht say to the dock?
"Yacht's (what's) up, Doc?"

What did the pitcher say to the cup?
"I'll have none of your lip."

When is it bad luck to have a black cat follow you?
When you are a mouse.

What is a person who steals Honda bikes?
A Honda-taker (undertaker).

What do you get if your sheep studies karate?
A lamb chop.

What kind of skates wear out quickly?
Cheapskates (cheap skates).

How do fireflies start a race?
When someone says, "Ready, set, glow!"

What is the best way to win a race?
Run faster than anybody else.

Where does Superman get the kind of food he needs to make him strong?
At the supermarket.

Why do you run faster when you have a cold?
You have a racing pulse and a running nose.

What kind of sandwich speaks for itself?
A tongue sandwich.

If your watch is broken, why can't you go fishing?
Because you don't have the time.

What would you do with a wombat?
Hit a womball!

What is the best way to communicate with a fish?
Drop him a line.

What did one fish say to the other?
"If you keep your big mouth shut, you won't get caught."

What game do girls dislike?
Soccer (sock her).

What famous prize do cats win?
The A-cat-emy (Academy) Award.

Why are dogs experts on trees?
They have to be if they don't want to bark up the wrong one.

If you're crazy about chess, why should you keep away from squirrels?
Because squirrels eat chestnuts (chess nuts).

A dog was tied to a 15-foot rope, but he walked 30 feet. How come?
The rope wasn't tied to anything.

What did the dog say when it was scratched by the cat?
Nothing. Dogs can't talk.

What is a cold war?
A snowball fight.

Why did the rooster refuse to fight?
Because he was chicken.

Why are mountain climbers curious?
They always want to take another peak (peek).

What goes 99-thump, 99-thump, 99-thump?
A centipede with a wooden leg.

What is a stupid mummy?
A dummy mummy.

Why did the mummy leave his tomb after 2,000 years?
He thought he was old enough to leave home.

What happens to old horses?
They become nags.

Why do turkeys eat so little?
Because they are always stuffed.

Why were the elephants the last animals to leave the ark?
They had to pack their trunks.

Why are shaggy dogs useful to have around the house?
Roll them around the floor and you have a good dust mop.

Why couldn't the dog catch his tail?
Because it is hard to make ends meet these days.

Why aren't horses well dressed?
Because they wear shoes but no socks.

What is the best exercise for losing weight?
Pushing yourself away from the table.

Why was the skeleton a coward?
Because he had no guts.

What would you call a bald Koala?
Fred Bear!

Why do skeletons drink a lot of milk?
Because it is good for the bones.

Why did the wife understand her invisible husband so well?
Because she could see right through him.

If Fortune had a daughter, what would her name be?
Misfortune (Miss Fortune).

What did the bow tie say to the boy?
"You double-crossed me."

What did the window say to the Venetian blind?
"If it weren't for you, it would be curtains for me."

Why are lollipops like racehorses?
The more you lick them the faster they go.

How can you make a slow horse fast?
Don't give him any food.

What did one horse say to the other horse?
"I forget your name but your pace (face) is familiar."

Why did the stale girl loaf of bread slap the stale boy loaf of bread?
Because he tried to get fresh.

What insect lives on nothing?
A moth because it eats holes.

Why did the bald man put a rabbit on his head?
Because he wanted a head of hare (hair).

Why was Adam known to be a good runner?
He was the first in the human race.

If two people had a race and one had sand in his shoe but the other did not, who would win?
The one with the sand in his shoe — if it was quicksand.

A cabbage, a **tap** and a tomato had a race. How did it go?
*The cabbage was ahead, the **tap** was running, and the tomato tried to ketchup.*

What is a sorcerer who casts only good spells?
A charming fellow.

Why shouldn't you listen to people who have just come out of the swimming pool?
Because they are all wet.

What kind of bell doesn't ring?
A dumbell.

Why do ducks look so sad?
When they preen their feathers, they get down in the mouth.

What is long and yellow and always points north?
A magnetic banana.

What do you call musical insects?
Humbugs!

Why are birds poor?
Because money doesn't grow on trees.

Why is a scrambled egg like a losing football team?
Because both are beaten.

What is the proper way to address the king of the ghosts?
"Your ghostliness."

Why couldn't the mountain climber call for help?
Because he was hanging by his teeth.

Why are owls brave?
Because they don't give a hoot about anything.

DOCTOR.... DOCTOR....

Patient: A crab just bit my toe.
Doctor: Which one?
Patient: I don't know. All crabs look alike to me.

Doctor: What seems to be the trouble?
Patient: I swallowed a clock last week.
Doctor: Good grief. Why didn't you come to see me before?
Patient: I didn't want to alarm anybody.

Nurse: Doctor, there's an invisible man in the waiting room.
Doctor: Tell him I can't see him.

Doctor: Have your eyes been checked lately?
Patient: No, they've always been plain blue.

Patient: Doctor, I get the feeling that people don't give a hoot about anything I say.
Psychiatrist: So?

Mother (on phone): Doctor, doctor. My son has swallowed a bullet. What shall I do?
Doctor: Don't point him at anybody.

Doctor: What is the problem?
Patient: I swallowed a roll of film.
Doctor: Don't worry. Nothing serious will develop.

Mrs. Jones: I'm sorry to bother you on such a terrible night, Doctor.
Doctor: That's all right. I had another patient down the road, so I thought I'd kill two birds with one stone.

Doctor: Ouch! OUCH!
Mother: Johnny, please say "ah" so the nice doctor can take his finger out of your mouth.

Doctor: How do you feel today?
Patient: Very much better, thank you. The only thing still bothering me is my breathing.
Doctor: We'll try to find something to stop that.

Patient: You were right, Doctor, when you said you would have me on my feet walking around in no time.
Doctor: Good. When did you start walking?
Patient: Right after I sold my car to pay your bill.

Patient: My head is bunged up, my sinuses need draining and my chest feels like lead. Can you help me?
Doctor: You need a plumber, not a doctor.

Patient: Doctor, you must help me. I can't remember anything.
Doctor: How long has this been going on?
Patient: How long has what been going on?

An excited woman telephoned her doctor: "Doctor, doctor, my husband swallowed a mouse. What shall I do?"

"Wave a piece of cheese in front of his mouth until I get there."

Fifteen minutes later he arrived at the house to find the woman waving a sardine in front of her husband's mouth.

"I said a piece of cheese, not a sardine!" exclaimed the doctor.

"I know you did," the woman replied. "But I have to get the cat out first."

Doctor: What is the trouble?
Patient: I think I'm a dog.
Doctor: How long has this been going on?
Patient: Ever since I was a puppy.

39

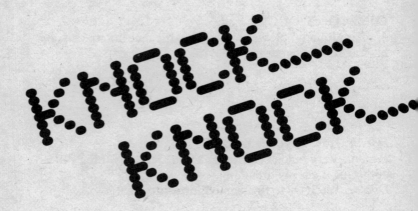

Who's there?
Orange juice.
Orange juice who?
Orange juice going to talk to me?

Who's there?
Osborn.
Osborn who?
Osborn today—it's my birthday!

Who's there?
Pasture.
Pasture who?
Pasture bedtime, isn't it?

Who's there?
Pecan.
Pecan who?
Pecan (pick on) somebody your own size!

Who's there?
Pharaoh.
Pharaoh who?
Pharaoh 'nuff.

Who's there?
Philippa.
Philippa who?
Philippa bathtub, I'm dirty.

Who's there?
Phyllis.
Phyllis who?
Phyllis in on the news.

Who's there?
Ping pong.
Ping pong who?
''Ping pong, the witch is dead . . .''

Who's there?
Plato.
Plato who?
Plato spaghetti and meatballs, please.

Who's there?
Police.
Police who?
Police open the door.

Who's there?
Possum.
Possum who?
Possum peace pipe.

Who's there?
Punch.
Punch who?
Not me—I just got here!

Who's there?
Quacker.
Quacker who?
Quacker 'nother bad joke and I'm leaving.

Who's there?
Quebec.
Quebec who?
Quebec to the end of the line.

Who's there?
Quiet Tina.
Quiet Tina who?
Quiet Tina courtroom.

Who's there?
Rabbit.
Rabbit who?
Rabbit up neatly. It's a present.

THAT'S REALLY FAR OUT!

What is as annoying as a roaring river?
A babbling brook.

What is yellow, soft and goes round and round?
A long-playing omelette.

What happens to an author after he dies?
He becomes a ghost writer.

Why did the invisible man go crazy?
Out of sight, out of mind.

Why did the kid cut a hole in the top of his umbrella?
So he could see when it stopped raining.

What is the difference between the North Pole and the South Pole?
The whole world.

What did the balloon say to the pin?
"Hi ya, Buster!"

What did the fireman say when the church caught on fire?
"Holy smoke!"

What kind of cats live in churches?
Holy cats!

Why did the absent minded professor put glue on his head?
Because he thought it would help things stick in his mind.

What trees do fortune tellers look at?
Palms.

What should you do with old fingernails?
File them.

What did the little kid answer when the teacher said, "Order, children, order!"?
"I'll have a hamburger with ketchup."

What is a sleeping child?
A kidnapper.

What is a very popular perfume?
A best smeller.

Where does afternoon always come before morning?
In the dictionary.

When are people like eyeglasses?
When they make spectacles of themselves.

Why did the man put his car in the oven?
Because he wanted a hot rod.

Why did the boy jump up and down on the letter?
He heard that you have to stamp letters or the post office won't send them.

If you cross a dog and a cat, what do you get?
An animal that chases itself.

43

What do you do with a green monster?
Wait till he ripens.

What sits on the bottom of the sea and shakes?
A nervous wreck.

What is a witch doctor's mistake?
A voodoo boo-boo.

What kind of jokes did Einstein make?
Wisecracks.

At what time of day was Adam born?
A little before Eve.

Why did the cricketer blink his eyelashes all day?
He needed batting practice.

When is the best time to buy budgies?
When they're going cheap!

What did the little kid do with the dead battery?
He buried it.

Why did the mad chef throw the chicken off the balcony?
Because he wanted to make egg drop soup.

What occurs once in every minute, twice in every moment, but not once in a thousand years?
The letter M.

What are the six main seasons?
Summer, autumn, winter, spring, salt and pepper.

What is a locomotive?
A crazy reason for doing something.

What do you have if you cross a witch and a millionaire?
A witch (rich) person.

What would you get if you crossed a skunk and an eagle?
An animal that stunk to high heaven.

How can you make varnish disappear?
Take out the R.

Is a unicorn male or female?
Female. The unicorn is a myth (Miss).

What time is it when a knight looks at his belly button?
It is the middle of the night (knight).

Where does a liar sleep?
In a bunk bed.

Which astronaut wears the biggest helmet?
The one with the biggest head.

What does an astronaut do when he gets angry?
He blasts off.

What do people do in a clock factory?
They make faces all day.

What do you call a person who looks over your shoulder
while you are eating at the lunch counter?
A counterspy.

What is purple and conquered the world?
Alexander the Grape.

What travels around the world but stays in a corner?
A stamp.

Why did the horses go on strike?
To get more horsepower.

Whose cow talks Russian?
Ma's cow (Moscow).

Why did the cowboy's car stop?
It had Injun (engine) trouble.

What did the explorer say when he saw the Pacific Ocean
for the first time?
"Long time no see (sea)."

Are you crazy if you talk to yourself?
Not unless you answer.

What is the difference between a counterfeit £10 note and a
crazy rabbit?
One is bad money, the other is a mad bunny.

What is the difference between a cloud and a spanked
child?
One pours down rain, the other roars with pain.

If you cross a lion and a monkey, what do you have?
A swinging lion.

If you cross a camera and a mirror, what do you get?
A camera that takes pictures of itself.

What do you get if you cross a jumbo jet and a kangaroo?
A plane that makes short hops.

What would you get if you crossed a pigeon, a frog, and a
prehistoric monster?
A pigeon-toed (toad) dinosaur.

Why did it take three husky Boy Scouts to help the little old lady across the street?
Because she didn't want to go.

What do you call an ocean plantation?
A pharmacy (farm-sea).

What holds the moon up?
Moonbeams.

Why is a grape religious?
Because it comes from divine (the vine).

Where do good pigs go when they die?
To a sty in the sky.

What did one angel say to the other angel?
"Halo."

Where can you buy cheap, ancient elephants?
At a mammoth sale!

What kind of clothes did Cinderella wear?
Wish and wear clothes.

Why does the Statue of Liberty stand?
Because she can't sit down.

If a millionaire sits on his gold, who sits on silver?
The Lone Ranger.

Why did the pirate put a chicken where he buried his treasure?
Because eggs (X) marks the spot.

What do you get when you cross a lion and a parrot?
I don't know, but if it wants a cracker, you'd better give it one.

How many balls of string would it take to reach the moon?
One, if it were long enough.

Why won't people ever go to the moon for their holiday?
Because it lacks atmosphere.

What kind of insects live on the moon?
Lunatics (lunar ticks).

Why are false teeth like stars?
Because they come out at night.

What did the stamp say to the envelope?
"I've become attached to you."

What did the envelope say to the stamp?
"Stick with me and we'll go places."

When do monster mothers receive gifts?
On Mummy's Day.

What kind of clock is crazy?
A cuckoo clock.

What has four eyes but can't see?
The Mississippi.

How do you make an elephant float?
Take two scoops of ice cream, coke, and add one elephant.

What dish is out of this world?
A flying saucer.

How can you get a cow into a frying pan?
Use shortening.

Is Ghostland a state?
  No, it's a terror-tory (territory).

What weighs a thousand pounds, has four legs, flies, and is yellow?
  Two five-hundred pound canaries.

How far can you go into a forest?
  Only halfway—after that you would be coming out.

What is the end of everything?
  The letter G.

Why is writing called handwriting?
  If people wrote with their feet, we would have to call it footwriting.

If a parrot had two A-levels, where would it go?
To the Poly-technic!

What did people say when the man got out of his rocking chair after 20 years?
  "He must be off his rocker."

What is yellow and swims underwater?
  A yellow submarine.

Why did the one-eyed chicken cross the road?
  Because there was a Bird's Eye factory across the street.

Why did the chicken cross the road twice?
  Because she was a double-crosser.

Why did the chicken go just halfway across the road?
  She wanted to lay it on the line.

Why can't you hit a stove a mile away?
   Because it is out of range.

What goes up and never comes down?
   Your age.

What did one angel say to the other?
   "What's harpening (happening)?"

Why did the old angel die?
   He had a harp (heart) attack.

How do Iranians speak on the telephone?
   Persian-to-Persian (person-to-person).

Why did the man buy a set of tools?
   Everyone said he had a screw loose.

What did the boy vampire say to the girl vampire?
   "I like your blood type."

What did the girl battery say to the boy battery?
   "I get a big charge out of you."

What did the boy accordion say to the girl accordion?
   "Every time I squeeze you I hear music."

What did the girl volcano say to the boy volcano?
   "Do you lava (love) me like I lava you?"

What goes on in a planetarium?
   An all-star show.

What colours would you paint the sun and the wind?
   The sun rose and the wind blue (blew).

Where do flowers come from?
The stalk (stork) brings them.

Why did the girl stand on a ladder when she learned how to sing?
Because she wanted to reach the high notes.

What happens to ducks who fly upside down?
They quack up!

Why did the man climb up to the chandelier?
He was a light sleeper.

What is big and red and eats rocks?
A big red rock eater.

What is the best year for a kangaroo?
Leap year.

When do you get that run-down feeling?
When a car hits you.

When does a river flood?
When it gets too big for its bridges (britches).

Why did the chicken cross the road?
With traffic the way it is today, probably to commit suicide.

What happened to Humpty Dumpty after he had a great fall?
He was made into an egg salad sandwich for all the king's men.

What would you have if a young goat fell into a blender?
A mixed-up kid.

Why doesn't Saint Nicholas shave?
Every time he tries, he nicks himself.

Who's there?
Raleigh.
Raleigh who?
Raleigh round the flag, boys.

Who's there?
Rapunzel.
Rapunzel who?
"Rapunzel troubles in your old kit bag and smile, smile, smile . . ."

Who's there?
Razor.
Razor who?
Razor hands—this is a stick-up!

Who's there?
Red.
Red who?
Red peppers. Isn't that a hot one?

Who's there?
Rhoda.
Rhoda who?
"Row, row, Rhoda boat . . ."

Who's there?
Robin.
Robin who?
Robin the piggy bank again?

Who's there?
Rocky.
Rocky who?
"Rocky bye baby on the tree top . . ."

Who's there?
Roland.
Roland who?
Roland stone gathers no moss.

Who's there?
Rufus.
Rufus who?
Rufus leaking and I'm getting wet.

Who's there?
Sabina.
Sabina who?
Sabina long time since I've seen you.

Who's there?
Mischa.
Mischa who?
Mischa a lot.

Who's there?
Sacha.
Sacha who?
Sacha fuss, just because I knocked at your door.

Who's there?
Sadie.
Sadie who?
Sadie things I like to hear.

Who's there?
Safari.
Safari who?
Safari so good.

Who's there?
Sam and Janet.
Sam and Janet who?
"Sam and Janet evening, you will meet a stranger . . ."

Who's there?
Sarah.
Sarah who?
Sarah doctor in the house?

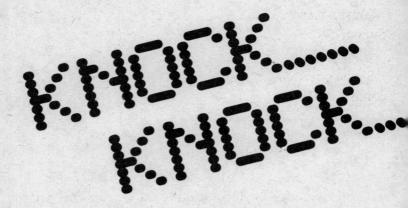

Who's there?
Saul.
Saul who?
"Saul the King's horses and Saul the King's men . . ."

Who's there?
Says.
Says who?
Says me, that's who!

Who's there?
Schatzi.
Schatzi who?
Schatzi way the ball bounces.

Who's there?
Scissor.
Scissor who?
Scissor and Cleopatra.

Who's there?
Scold.
Scold who?
Scold outside.

Who's there?
Seymour.
Seymour who?
Seymour if you'd open the door .

Who's there?
Sharon.
Sharon who?
Sharon share alike.

Who's there?
Sheila.
Sheila who?
"Sheila be coming round the mountain when she comes . . ."

Who's there?
Sherry.
Sherry who?
Sherry dance?

Who's there?
Sherwood.
Sherwood who?
Sherwood like to help you out; which way did you come in?

Who's there?
Shirley.
Shirley who?
Shirley you must know me by now.

Who's there?
Sicily.
Sicily who?
Sicily question.

Who's there?
Sizzle.
Sizzle who?
Sizzle hurt me more than it hurts you.

Who's there?
Soda.
Soda who?
Soda you!

Who's there?
Sonia.
Sonia who?
"Sonia paper moon . . ."

Who's there?
Spider.
Spider who?
Spider what everyone says, I like you.

Oh, no! Not again.

Where do fish raise money on their valuables?
At the prawnshop.

What would you call two bananas?
A pair of slippers.

What would you call the life story of a car?
An autobiography.

What part of a clock is always old?
The second hand.

What do you get if you cross a squirrel and a kangaroo?
An animal that carries nuts in its pocket.

What is a banged-up used car?
A car in first-crash condition.

What does Santa Claus do when it is not Christmas?
*He is probably a farmer because he always says,
"Hoe, hoe, hoe!"*

Why is a book like a king?
Because they both have pages.

What is black and white and red all over?
A newspaper.

What is black and white and red all over?
A sunburned zebra.

What causes baldness?
Lack of hair.

What animals are well educated?
Fish, because they go around in schools.

What is black and white and red all over?
A skunk with nappy rash.

What is black and white and red all over?
A blushing penguin.

What is the correct height for people to stand?
Over two feet.

What does a dog get when it graduates from dog school?
A pedigree.

What is the difference between a dog and a flea?
A dog can have fleas but a flea can't have dogs.

Why are men going bald at an older age these days?
Because they're wearing their hair longer.

Who invented the telephone?
The Phoenicians (phone-itions).

What are the most faithful insects?
Ticks. Once they find friends, they stick to them.

What would happen if you swallowed your knife and fork?
You would have to eat with your hands.

Where can you always find diamonds?
In a deck of cards.

What is an ocean?
Where buoy meets gull (boy meets girl).

What is green and pecks on trees?
Woody Wood Pickle.

What is a parasite?
Something you see in Paris.

What happened when Frankenstein met a girl monster?
They fell in love at first fright.

What did the boy Frankenstein say to the girl
Frankenstein?
"You are so electrocute."

How can you tell if a ghost is about to faint?
He goes pale as a sheet.

What did one invisible man say to the other invisible man?
"It's nice not to see you again."

When is an army like a sales clerk making out a bill?
When it is ready to charge.

Why did the three little pigs leave home?
Because their father was a big boar (bore).

Why do cats sleep better in summer than in winter?
Because summer brings the caterpillar (cat a pillow).

Why did the girl sit on her watch?
She wanted to be on time.

What 8-letter word has one letter in it?
Envelope.

What did one car say to the other?
"You look familiar. Haven't we bumped into each other before?"

What two words have thousands of letters in them?
Post Office.

Why do hurricanes travel so fast?
Because if they travelled slowly, we'd have to call them slow-i-canes.

If fish lived on land, where would they live?
In Finland.

If two's company and three's a crowd, what is four and five?
Nine.

What are the three swiftest means of communication?
Telephone, telegraph and tell-a-secret.

What is an ultimate?
The last person you marry.

"Did you hear the story about the smog?"
"You don't have to tell me, it's all over town."

What is big and purple and lies in the sea?
Grape Britain.

What is a ship for good writers?
Penmanship.

What is the front part of a geography book?
The table of continents (contents).

How can you eat and study at the same time?
Eat alphabet soup.

When are people smartest?
*During the day, because when the sun shines
everything is brighter.*

What did the little calf say to the haystack?
"Are you my folder (father)?"

Why are we sure that Indians were the first people in
North America?
Because they had reservations.

What did one magnet say to the other magnet?
"I find you very attractive."

What did one tap say to the other tap?
"You're a big drip."

What did one insect say to the other insect?
"Stop bugging me."

What happens to tyres when they get old?
They are retired.

What animal is grey and has a trunk?
A mouse going on holiday.

What did the stocking with the hole say to the shoe?
"Well, I'll be darned!"

What did the necktie say to the hat?
"You go on ahead. I'll hang around for a while."

Why did the man keep a ruler on his newspaper?
Because he wanted to get the story straight.

What's the best way to count cows?
On a cow-culator.

Why can you always believe a ruler?
Because it is on the level.

Why did the boy take the ruler to bed?
He wanted to see how long he slept.

Where does Friday come before Thursday?
In the dictionary.

What did the wig say to the head?
"I've got you covered."

Why did the boy put his head in the washing machine?
He wanted to have that "wet look."

Why did the boy put his head in the dryer?
Because he wanted to have that "dry look."

Where can you find cards on a ship?
On the deck.

What radio has a crewcut?
A short-wave radio.

If there were no food left, what could people do?
Country people could eat their forest preserves and city people could have their traffic jams.

Why do people laugh up their sleeves?
That's where their funny bones are.

What did the big carburettor say to the little carburettor?
"Don't inhale so fast or you'll choke."

What did one windscreen wiper say to the other windscreen wiper?
"Isn't it a shame we seem to meet only when it rains?"

Why did the cat join the Red Cross?
So it could become a first-aid kit.

How can you say rabbit without using the letter R?
Bunny.

Why did the girl put sugar under her pillow?
She wanted sweet dreams.

Who takes longer to get ready for a trip—an elephant or a rooster?
The elephant. He has to pack a trunk while the rooster only takes his comb.

What is a ringleader?
The first person in the bath.

When do the leaves begin to turn?
The night before a test.

When do your car's brakes work best?
In the morning when it's breakfast (brake fast) time.

How can you get out of a locked room with a piano in it?
Play the piano until you find the right key and you can get out.

What happens when two oxen bump into each other?
You have an oxident (accident).

Why were the inventors of the aeroplane correct in thinking they could fly?
Because they were Wright (right).

Why do scientists look for things twice?
Because they research (re-search) everything.

What person can jump higher than a house?
Anyone. A house can't jump.

What is the difference between a man and a running dog?
One wears trousers, the other pants.

What kind of clothing does a pet dog wear?
A petticoat.

What did the shirt say to the trousers?
"Meet me at the clothesline. That's where I hang out."

What did the book say to the librarian?
"Can I take you out?"

What did the girl calendar say to the other girl calendar?
"I have more dates than you do."

Why did the girl tear the calendar?
Because she wanted to take a month off.

What is a dentist's office?
A filling station.

What would happen if you ate yeast and polish?
You would rise and shine.

Waiter, waiter, this goulash is terrible.
Sir, our chef has been making goulash since before you were born.
Maybe so, but why did he save it for me?

Waiter, waiter, that crust on the apple pie was tough.
That wasn't the crust, Sir, that was the paper plate.

Hey, waiter, hey!
All right, Sir, but we'll have to send out for it.

Waiter, waiter, it's been half an hour since I ordered the turtle soup.
Yes, Sir, but you know how slow turtles are.

Waiter: *Hawaii*, mister. You must be *Hungary*?
Customer: Yes, *Siam*. But I can't *Rumania* here for long. *Venice* dinner being served?
Waiter: I'll *Russia* everything. What will you have? *Turkey* fried in *Greece*?
Customer: Whatever is ready. But can't you *Jamaica* cook do it fast?
Waiter: *Odessa* laugh, *Juneau*. But *Alaska*.
Customer: In the meantime I'll have a cup of *Java* with a *Cuba* sugar.
Waiter: Don't be *Sicily*. *Sweden* it yourself. I'm only here to *Serbia*.
Customer: *Denmark* up my *Czech*. I don't *Bolivia* know who I am.
Waiter: I don't *Kenya* and I don't *Caribbean* about you.
Customer: *Samoa* wisecracks. What's got *India*? Do you think this arguing *Alps* business?
Waiter: You're a big *Spain* in the neck. *Abyssinia*.

Waiter, waiter, I've been waiting here for over an hour.
So what, Sir. I've been waiting her for over 30 years.

Waiter, waiter, there's no turtle in this turtle soup.
Of course. If you look close you'll see that there is also no horse in the horseradish.

Waiter, waiter, there's a fly in my soup.
Well, it's better than having no meat at all.

Waiter, waiter, there's a fly in my soup.
Don't worry, the spider on the bread will take care of it.

Waiter, waiter, I don't care for all the flies in this restaurant.
Very well, Sir, just point out the ones you don't like and I'll put them out.

Waiter, waiter, why is this doughnut all smashed up?
You said you wanted a cup of coffee and a doughnut and step on it, Sir, so I did.

Waiter, waiter, I'll have a hamburger.
With pleasure.
No, with pickles and onions.

Waiter, waiter, have you any wild duck?
No, Sir, but we can take a tame one and irritate him for you.

Waiter, waiter, this meat isn't fit for a pig.
I'll take it back then, Sir, and bring you some that is.

Customer: I can't eat this soup.
Waiter: Sorry, Sir. I'll call the manager.
Customer: Mr Manager, I can't eat this soup.
Manager: Sorry, Sir, I'll call the chef.
Customer: Chef, I can't eat this soup.
Chef: What's wrong with it?
Customer: Nothing. I just don't have a spoon.

Who's there?
Stan.
Stan who?
Stan back, I'm going to sneeze!

Who's there?
Statue.
Statue who?
Statue? This is me.

Who's there?
Stefan.
Stefan who?
Stefan it quick before it crawls up my leg.

Who's there?
Stepfather.
Stepfather who?
One stepfather and I'll let you have it.

Who's there?
Stopwatch.
Stopwatch who?
Stopwatch you're doing this minute!

Who's there?
Stu.
Stu who?
Stu late to ask questions.

Who's there?
Sultan.
Sultan who?
Sultan pepper.

Who's there?
Summertime.
  Summertime who?
Summertime you can be a big pest.

                    Who's there?
                    Sybil.
                      Sybil who?
                    Sybil Simon met a pieman.

Who's there?
Tad.
  Tad who?
Tad-s all, folks!

                    Who's there?
                    Tamara.
                      Tamara who?
                    Tamara the world.

Who's there?
Tank.
  Tank who?
You're welcome.

                    Who's there?
                    Dimension.
                      Dimension who?
                    Dimension it.

Who's there?
Teachers.
  Teachers who?
Teachers (three cheers) for the Queen.

                    Who's there?
                    Tennis.
                      Tennis who?
                    Tennis five plus five.

Who's there?
Tex.
  Tex who?
Tex two to tango.

BRAIN TEASERS

What sport do horses like playing?
Stable tennis!

Why did the little cookie cry?
> *Because its mother was a wafer (away for) a long time.*

Why does Tarzan yell?
> *He is so strong that every time he beats his chest, it hurts.*

When can you throw a watch out the window, go down three flights of stairs, and catch it?
> *When it is 10 minutes slow.*

What 5-letter word has 6 left when you take 2 letters away?
> *Sixty.*

What is black when it is clean and white when it is dirty?
> *A blackboard.*

If two wrongs don't make a right, what did two rights make?
> *An aeroplane.*

What is the best way to make time race?
> *Use the spur of the moment.*

Why was the bride unhappy with the first cake she baked?
Because her husband took it for granite (granted).

What is an angel in heaven?
A blessing in disguise (the skies).

What kind of cars come from Norway?
Norwegian fiords (Fords).

What comes in different flavours, shakes a lot and lives in the ocean?
A jellyfish.

What can a bird do that a man cannot do?
Take a bath in a saucer.

What is the difference between a horse and the weather?
One is reined up, the other rains down.

What do you call someone whose library books are overdue?
A book|-|keeper.

What instrument lets you see monsters?
A horror-scope.

Why can't you read a stupid person's mind?
The type is too small.

What do you call someone who helps on a farm?
A pharmacist (farm assist).

What did the skunk say when the wind changed?
"It all comes back to me now."

What did the shy pebble say?
"I wish I were a little bolder (boulder)."

Why does a thoroughbred dog get hotter in summer than a mongrel dog?
A thoroughbred dog has more pedigrees.

What are the last three hairs on a dog's tail called?
Dog hairs.

Why was the geometry teacher boring?
Because he was a square and talked in circles.

What do you get if you stand too close to the fireplace?
Hearth (heart) burn.

Why wouldn't the kid study history?
Because he thought it better to let bygones be bygones.

Why is a turkey more evil than a chicken?
Because a turkey is always a'gobblin' (goblin).

How do you get two quarts of milk into a one quart container?
Condense it.

If you cross an owl and a goat, what do you have?
A hootenanny.

If you crossed an axe and a stick, what would you get?
A chopstick.

What is mind?
No matter.

What is matter?
Never mind.

A man drove all the way from New York to San Francisco without knowing he had a flat tyre. How is that possible?
It was his spare tyre that was flat.

Once upon a time there was a king. Set before him were three glasses. Two of them were filled with water. The other one was empty. What was the king's name?
Philip (fill up) the Third.

On what day of the year did soldiers start wars in history?
March fourth.

Why was the United Nations worried when the waiter dropped a platter of turkey on the floor?
It meant the fall of Turkey, the ruin of Greece, and the break-up of China.

What is the difference between a man parking his car and a man smashing dishes?
One sets the brakes, the other breaks the sets.

What is a dieter's motto?
"If at first you don't recede; diet again."

Why did the farmer give his sick pig a piece of sugar?
Haven't you ever heard of sugar-cured ham.

What is black, shiny, lives in trees and is very dangerous?
A crow with a machine gun.

What is too much for one, enough for two, but nothing for three?
A secret.

If all the letters of the alphabet were invited to a tea party, what letters would be late?
The letters U, V, W, X, Y and Z. They all come after T (tea).

How are the deaths of a sculptor and a barber different?
One makes faces and busts; the other curls up and dyes (dies).

Why couldn't Batman go fishing?
Because Robin ate all the worms.

If you add a father, a mother and a baby, what do you get?
Two and one to carry.

If you see a counterfeit £10 note lying in the street, should you leave it or pick it up?
Better pick it up. You might get arrested for passing it.

What is rhubarb?
Celery with high blood pressure.

When does eleven plus two equal one?
On a watch face.

When was tennis mentioned in the Bible?
When Joseph served in Pharaoh's court.

What is worse than raining cats and dogs?
Hailing taxis.

There were 99 people on a boat. It turned over. How many were left?
66.

What kind of bed is a three-season bed?
One without a spring.

What sick bird could be unlawful?
An ill-eagle (illegal).

What is the difference between a mule and a postage stamp?

One you lick with a stick, the other you stick with a lick.

Where would a zoo keeper hang his washing?
On the clothes lion.

What is green and goes "click, click, click"?

A ball-point pickle.

What is green and can jump a mile a minute?

A grasshopper with hiccups.

What does not move when it is fast but moves when it is not fast?

A motorboat tied up at a dock.

What is junk?

Something you save for years and throw away just before you need it.

What is the difference between a cat and a comma?

A cat has claws at the end of its paws, a comma has a pause at the end of its clause.

When Adam introduced himself to Eve, what three words did he use which read the same backwards and forwards?

"Madam, I'm Adam."

If a boy broke his knee, where could he get a new one?

At the butcher shop where they sell kidneys (kid knees).

What is the difference between the back light of a car and a short story?

One is a tail light, the other a light tale.

What is the difference between a tree and a leopard?

One is rooted to the spot, the other is spotted to the root.

Big as a biscuit, deep as a cup, even a river cannot fill it up. What is it?
  A funnel.

Where are there more nobles than at court?
  In the library. All the books have titles.

Why did the man look for an automobile in the garden?
  He heard that his car had just come from the plant.

Why were the Dark Ages so dark?
  They had more knights (nights) in those days.

What did the wild game hunters say after a week in the jungle?
  Safari (so far) so good.

What is the difference between a hungry man and a greedy man?
  One longs to eat, the other eats too long.

What winter sport do you learn in the fall?
  Skiing.

What could you call the small rivers that flow into the Nile?
  Juveniles.

What did one flea say to the other flea?
  "Shall we walk or shall we take the dog?"

Why did the vet operate on the dog?
  Because a stitch in time saves canine (nine).

If you are going on a long hike in the desert, what should you carry?
  A thirst-aid kit.

What is a synonym?
A word you use when you can't spell the other one.

Why do you comb your hair before going to bed?
To make a good impression on the pillow.

Why did the gardener throw roses into the burning building?
He heard that flowers grew better in hot houses.

What goes Zzub, Zzub, Zzub?
A bee flying backwards!

What do you drop when you need it and take back when you don't?
An anchor.

If you pull it, it's a cane; if you push it, it's a tent. What is it?
An umbrella.

What does a lamp-post become when the lamp is removed?
A lamp lighter.

Why is a black chicken smarter than a white one?
Because a black chicken can lay a white egg, but a white chicken can't lay a black one.

What is the hardest train to catch?
The 12:50 because it is ten to one if you catch it.

What is the difference between a pen and a pencil?
You push a pen, but a pencil has to be led (lead).

A man came home late without his key and found all the windows and doors locked. How did he get in?
He ran round and round the house until he was all in.

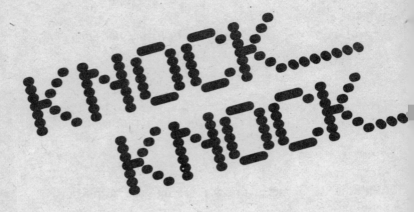

Who's there?
Thayer.
Thayer who?
Thayer thorry and I won't throw this pie in your face.

Who's there?
Thea.
Thea who?
Thea later, alligator.

Who's there?
Theodore.
Theodore who?
Theodore is closed, open up!

Who's there?
Theresa.
Theresa who?
Theresa fly in my soup.

Who's there?
Therese.
Therese who?
Therese many a slip twixt the cup and the lip.

Who's there?
Thermos.
Thermos who?
Thermos be a better way.

Who's there?
Thumb.
Thumb who?
Thumb like it hot and thumb like it cold.

Who's there?
Thumping.
Thumping who?
Thumping green and slimy is climbing up your neck.

Who's there?
Tibet.
Tibet who?
Early Tibet and early to rise . . .

Who's there?
Toby.
Toby who?
Toby or not Toby.

Who's there?
Thaddeus.
Thaddeus who?
Thaddeus question.

Who's there?
Tom Sawyer.
Tom Sawyer who?
Tom Sawyer underwear.

Who's there?
Toothy.
Toothy who?
Toothy, the day after Monday.

Who's there?
Torch.
Torch who?
Torch you would never ask.

Who's there?
Toucan.
Toucan who?
Toucan play at this game.

Who's there?
Toyota.
Toyota who?
Toyota be a law against knock-knock jokes.

DOCTOR.... DOCTOR.

Patient: Doctor, doctor I feel like a pair of curtains.
Doctor: Well, pull yourself together then.

Patient: Doctor, doctor, I've just swallowed a sheep.
Doctor: How do you feel?
Patient: Very ba-a-a-d.

Patient: Doctor, doctor, everyone thinks I'm a liar.
Doctor: I don't believe you.

Patient: Doctor, doctor, I feel like a spoon.
Doctor: Sit down and don't stir.

Patient: Doctor, doctor, I have an awful problem. I keep stealing things.
Doctor: Have you taken anything for it?

Patient: Doctor, doctor, I keep seeing pink elephants.
Doctor: Have you ever seen a psychiatrist?
Patient: No, just pink elephants.

Patient: Doctor, doctor, I feel like a cricket ball.
Doctor: How's that?
Patient: Oh, don't you start.

Patient: Doctor, doctor, I've got cucumbers growing out of my ears.
Doctor: My goodness. How did that happen?
Patient: Beats me. I planted carrots.

Patient: Thank you, Doctor. Now I feel like my old self again.
Doctor: In that case you'll need more treatment.

Doctor: Your cough sounds much better today.
Patient: It should. I practised all night.

Patient: Can a person be in love with an elephant?
Doctor: No.
Patient: Do you know anyone who wants to buy a very large engagement ring?

Doctor: Please breathe out three times.
Patient: Is that so you can check my lungs?
Doctor: No, so I can clean my glasses.

Patient: Doctor, I understand that you are the greatest expert in the world for the cure of baldness. If you cure me, I'll give you anything you ask.
Doctor (after examining the patient): I have some good news and some bad news. First the bad news: I can't grow any more hair on your head. Now for the good news: I can shrink your head to fit the hair you've got.

Doctor: What seems to be the problem?
Patient: I eat dates.
Doctor: What's wrong with that?
Patient: Off calendars?

Doctor: What did you dream about last night?
Patient: Cricket.
Doctor: Didn't you dream about anything else?
Patient: What and miss my turn to bat?

Patient: I'm not well, Doctor.
Doctor: What seems to be the trouble?
Patient: I work like a horse, eat like a bird and I'm as tired as a dog.
Doctor: Sounds to me like you ought to see a vet not a doctor.

Man: Doctor, I'm worried about my brother. He thinks he's a lift.
Doctor: I'd better look at him. Send him up.
Man: I can't. He doesn't stop between floors.

DON'T LOOK AT THESE!

What do you call a Scottish parrot?
A Macaw.

What do you call Eskimo cows?
Eskimoos.

What do you get if you cross a centipede and a parrot?
A walkie-talkie.

What do you get if you cross a chick and a guitar?
A chicken that makes music when you pluck it.

What do you get if you cross a homing pigeon and a woodpecker?
A bird that not only delivers messages, but also knocks on the door.

What do you get if you cross a cocker spaniel, a poodle and a rooster?
A cockapoodledoo.

What do you get if you cross a canary and a tiger?
I don't know, but when it sings you'd better listen.

What do two oceans say when they meet?
They don't say anything, they just wave.

What is the best way to pitch a tent?
It depends—sometimes overhand and sometimes underhand.

What nationality is Santa Claus?
North Polish.

What is long and thin and goes, "Hith, Hith"?
A snake with a lisp.

If a buttercup is yellow, what colour is a hiccup?
Burple.

What do you call it when pigs do their laundry?
Hogwash!

What do liars do after they die?
Lie still.

If you crossed King Kong and a bell, what would you have?
A ding-dong King Kong.

How do you know that carrots are good for the eyes?
Have you ever seen a rabbit wearing spectacles?

What did the cannibal have for lunch?
Baked beings (beans).

What goes, "Clomp, clomp, clomp, squish. Clomp, clomp, clomp, squish"?
An elephant with a wet shoe.

Why did the boy's mother knit him three socks for Christmas?
Because he grew another foot.

Why should you stay calm when you meet a cannibal?
You don't want to get into a stew.

What would you get if Minnehaha married Santa Claus?
Minnehaha hoho.

What do you call a knife that cuts four loaves of bread at the same time?
A four-loaf cleaver (clover).

What is white outside, green inside, and hops?
A frog sandwich.

What is a ghoul's favourite food?
Goulash.

What wears a black cape, flies through the night, and bites?
A mosquito in a black cape.

What is a twip?
A twip is what a wabbit takes when he wides a twain.

Why shouldn't you sweep out a room?
The job is too big. Just sweep out the dirt and leave the room there.

Who invented spaghetti?
Someone who used his noodle.

Where do old Volkswagens go?
To the old Volks (folks) home.

How do mummies behave?
   In a grave manner.

What is on a ghost's bicycle wheels?
   Spooks (spokes).

What is a haunted wigwam?
   A creepy teepee.

Why did the ghost kid measure himself against the wall?
   Because he wanted to know if he gruesome (grew some).

If you cross a dog and an egg, what would you get?
   A pooched (poached) egg.

What is a piece of pie in Italian?
   A pizza pie.

What do bees do with all their honey?
   Cell (sell) it.

What do you get if you cross a clock and a chicken?
   An alarm cluck (clock).

What would you get if you crossed a dog and a waffle?
   A woofle.

What sound do two porcupines make when they kiss?
   "Ouch!"

How do mice kiss?
   Mouse-to-mouse (mouth-to-mouth).

How do you stop a dog from barking in the back seat of a car?
Make him sit up front.

What should you do with a blue monster?
Cheer him up.

If you cross ducks and cows, what would you have?
Quackers (crackers) and milk.

What does a person have to know before teaching tricks to a dog?
More than the dog.

Why did Robin Hood rob the rich?
Because the poor didn't have any money.

Why is an elephant grey, large, and wrinkled?
Because if he were small, white and round, he would be an aspirin.

What is green and dangerous?
A thundering herd of pickles.

Why do dragons sleep during the day?
So that they can fight knights (nights).

What is yellow, smooth and very dangerous?
Shark-infested custard.

Why would someone in jail want to catch the measles?
So he could break out.

What is the difference between an elephant and a jar of peanut butter?

The elephant doesn't stick to the roof of your mouth.

Why did the elephant lie in the middle of the road?

To trip the ants.

If you found a £10 note in every pocket of your coat, what would you have?

Someone else's coat.

Where do they store Chinese boats?

In a junkyard.

What would you get if Batman and Robin were run over by a herd of stampeding buffalo?

The Mashed (Masked) Crusaders.

How do you keep a rhinoceros from charging?

Take away his credit cards.

Why is a grouchy kindergarten teacher like a collection of old car parts?

She's a crank surrounded by a bunch of little nuts.

What is a fast tricycle?

A tot rod.

What is the best way to hunt bear?

With your clothes off.

What does a mummy child call its parents?

Mummy and Deady.

What did the boy octopus say to the girl octopus?
"I want to hold your hand, hand, hand, hand, hand, hand, hand, hand."

What should you say when you meet a monster with two heads?
"Hello, hello!"

What is the best way to talk to a vampire?
By long distance.

What kind of mistake does a ghost make?
A boo-boo.

Why did the projector blush?
It saw the filmstrip.

Why did the traffic light turn red?
So would you if you had to change in front of all those people.

What kind of feet does a mathematics teacher have?
Square feet.

When I get old and ugly, will you still talk to me?
Don't I?

What do you call a sunburn on your stomach?
Pot roast.

What is abcdefghijklmnopqrstuvwxyz, slurp?
Someone eating alphabet soup.

In what kind of home do the buffalo roam?
A very dirty one.

What is purple and goes "hmmm"?
An electric grape.

If you need a loan, who do you see in the bank?
The Loan Arranger (Lone Ranger).

What happened when the Scotsman went to buy clothes?
He got kilt (killed).

If an athlete gets athlete's foot, what does an astronaut get?
Missile toe.

Which is better to have, a cow or a bull?
A cow gives milk, but a bull always charges.

Why is a bride always out of luck on her wedding day?
Because she never marries the best man.

How did the patient get to the hospital so fast?
Flu.

Where does a two-ton gorilla sleep?
Anywhere he wants to.

What is free speech?
When you can use someone else's telephone.

What happened when the dentist and the manicurist had an argument?
They fought tooth and nail.

Who's there?
Tuna.
Tuna who?
Tuna your radio down, you're making too much noise.

Who's there?
Turnip.
Turnip who?
Turnip the heat. It's cold out here.

Who's there?
Tyrone.
Tyrone who?
Tyrone shoe laces. You're big enough now.

Who's there?
Uganda.
Uganda who?
Uganda get away with this.

Who's there?
Uriah.
Uriah who?
Keep Uriah on the ball.

Who's there?
Uruguay.
Uruguay who?
You go Uruguay and I'll go mine.

Who's there?
Usher.
Usher who?
Usher wish you would let me in.

Who's there?
Uta.
   Uta who?
Uta sight, uta mind.

            Who's there?
            Utica.
               Utica who?
               Utica high road and I'll take the low road.

Who's there?
Valencia. (Pronounced Va-*len*-see-ya)
   Valencia who?
Valencia pound, will you pay it back?

            Who's there?
            Vanilla.
               Vanilla who?
               Vanilla call the doctor.

Who's there?
Vassar girl.
   Vassar girl who?
Vassar girl like you doing in a place like this?

            Who's there?
            Vaughan.
               Vaughan who?
               "Vaughan day my prince will come . . ."

Who's there?
Vera.
   Vera who?
"Vera all the flowers gone . . ."

            Who's there?
            Viola.
               Viola who?
               Viola sudden you don't know me?

Who's there?
Aloysius. (Pronounced A-loo-ish-us)
   Aloysius who?
"Aloysius for Christmas is my two front teeth . . ."

Who's there?
Alaska.
Alaska who?
Alaska my mummy.

Who's there?
Violet.
Violet who?
Violet the cat out of the bag?

Who's there?
Virtue.
Virtue who?
Virtue get those big, brown eyes?

Who's there?
Voodoo.
Voodoo who?
Voodoo you think you are?

Who's there?
Waddle.
Waddle who?
Waddle you give me if I go away?

Who's there?
Wafer.
Wafer who?
Wafer a long time, but here I am again.

Who's there?
Wah.
Wah who?
Well, you don't have to get so excited about it!

Who's there?
Waiter.
Waiter who?
Waiter I get my hands on you!

Who's there?
Walnuts.
Walnuts who?
Walnuts around here.

          Who's there?
          Walter.
          Walter who?
          Walter-wall carpeting.

Who's there?
Wanda.
Wanda who?
Wanda buy some brushes?

          Who's there?
          Wannetta.
          Wannetta who?
          Wannetta time, please.

Who's there?
Warner.
Warner who?
Warner you coming out to play?

          Who's there?
          Warrior.
          Warrior who?
          Warrior been all my life?

Who's there?
Wash.
Wash who?
Wash you there, Charlie?

Who's there?
Water.
Water who?
Water be ashamed of yourself for living in a dump like this!

          Who's there?
          Watson.
          Watson who?
          Watson your mind?

WEIRD MONSTERS

Why did the musician strike the record with a hammer?
He wanted a hit record.

What did the woodchopper do when he didn't know the time?
He axed (asked) someone.

If a girl ate her mother and father, what would that make her?
An orphan.

Why did the dog run around in circles?
Because he was a watchdog and wanted to wind himself up.

Why was the puppy fat?
Because he always had a second yelping (helping).

What did the vegetable say when it was wrapped for another day?
"Curses, foiled again!"

What did Sir Lancelot wear to bed?
A nightgown (knight gown).

What does a 10 stone mouse say?
"Here, Kitty, Kitty."

Why do elephants paint their toenails red?
So that they can hide in the strawberry patch.

Where does Frankenstein's wife have her hair done?
At the ugly parlour.

Who was the first swinger?
Tarzan.

What is green and flies?
Super Pickle.

Why does Batman brush his teeth at least three times a day?
To prevent bat (bad) breath.

If you cross a pig and a young goat, what do you get?
A dirty kid.

What do you get if you cross a porcupine and a young goat?
A stuck-up kid.

What gives milk and says, "Oom, oom"?
A cow walking backwards.

What kind of boats do vampires take when they travel?
Blood vessels.

Why did the rabbit wear a shower cap?
Because he didn't want his hare (hair) to get wet.

Why did the kid roll rocks down the hill?
He wanted to see the Rolling Stones.

What branch of the army do babies join?
The infantry.

What would you call a knight caught in a windstorm?
A nightingale (knight in gale).

Why did the pig act up?
Because he was a big ham.

Chief Running Water had two sons. What were their names?
Hot and Cold.

Why did the astronomer hit himself on the head in the afternoon?
He wanted to see stars during the day.

What was Batman doing in the tree?
Looking for Robin's nest.

What kind of crew does a monster ship have?
A skeleton crew.

Why did the elephant swallow a camphor ball?
To keep moths out of his trunk.

Why did the farmer feed his cow money?
He wanted rich milk.

Why do you get a charge out of reading the newspaper?
Because it is full of current events.

What did the boots say to the cowboy?
"You ride, I'll go on foot."

What did the kid say when the dentist asked him what kind of filling he wanted?
"Chocolate."

Why did the playboy roll up the carpet?
He wanted to see the whole floor show.

Why did the potato farmer use a steam roller?
Because he wanted to grow mashed potatoes.

Why did the mad chef watch the lazy cow?
He liked to see the meat loaf.

Why did the secretary ask for a round envelope?
Because she wanted to mail a circular.

Why didn't Count Dracula get married?
Because he was a bat-chelor (bachelor).

Why did the nasty kid put ice cubes in his aunt's bed?
Because he wanted to make antifreeze.

Why did the girl aim a cannon at the peas?
Because her mother told her to shell them.

What animal eats and drinks with its tail?
All do. No animal takes off his tail when eating or drinking.

What did the invisible salesman say?
"What you don't see is what you don't get."

Why did the girl put her bed in the fireplace?
So that she could sleep like a log.

Why did the boy run down the block with a clock in his pocket?
He wanted to keep up with the times.

Why did the man put his pants on backwards?
Because he didn't know whether he was coming or going.

Why do witches ride brooms?
Because vacuum cleaners are too hard to fly.

Why did King Kong play with the flying saucer?
He thought it was a frisbee.

Why did the girl keep running around her bed?
She wanted to catch up on her sleep.

Why did the writer put his fingers in the alphabet soup?
He was trying to find the right words.

Why did the banker keep looking up at the sky?
To see if there was any change in the weather.

What did the Martian say when he landed in the flower bed?
"Take me to your weeder (leader)."

What did the chick say when the hen sat on an orange?
"Look at the orange marmalade (mamma laid)."

How would you describe the expression on a zombie's face?

Deadpan.

Do zombies like being dead?

Of corpse (Of course!)

Why did the lady jump in the ocean?

To get a wave in her hair.

What is a crazy duck?

A wacky quacky.

Why does William live on a mountain?

Because he is a hillbilly.

What would you call a female Indian chief who is always getting into trouble?

Mischief.

Why did the timid soul always take cold baths?

Because he didn't want to get into hot water.

What did one bird say to another as he saw a jet fly by?

"I bet I could fly that fast if my tail were on fire."

What did the pig say when the butcher grabbed him by the tail?

"That's the end of me!"

What did the 2,000-year-old boy say when he was dug up?

"I want my mummy!"

Why couldn't the mummy answer the telephone?

Because he was all tied up.

What did the man say when he found that he was going bald?

"Hair today and gone tomorrow!"

Why did the golfer wear two pairs of trousers?

Just in case he got a hole in one.

Who was the first man in space?

The man in the moon.

Why does an Indian wear feathers?

To keep his wigwam (wig warm).

Why did the baby goose think the car was its mother?

Because the car honked.

What is a doughnut?

A person who is crazy about money.

Why did the girl wear loud socks?

She didn't want her feet to fall asleep.

Why did the old man put wheels on his rocking chair?

Because he wanted to rock and roll.

What happened to Ray when he jumped off the Empire State Building?

He is now called X-ray.

Why did the pelican put his leg in his mouth when he ate out?

He wanted to foot the bill.

Who's there?
Wayne.
Wayne who?
Wayne are you coming over to my house?

Who's there?
Weevil.
Weevil who?
Weevil work it out.

Who's there?
Weirdo.
Weirdo who?
Weirdo you think you're going?

Who's there?
Wendy.
Wendy who?
"Wendy wind blows, the cradle will rock . . ."

Who's there?
Wheelbarrow.
Wheelbarrow who?
Wheelbarrow some money and go on a trip.

Who's there?
Who.
Who who?
You sound like an owl.

Who's there?
Wicked.
Wicked who?
Wicked make beautiful music together.

Who's there?
Will you remember me in a week?
Yes.
Will you remember me in a month?
Yes.
Will you remember me in a year?
Yes.
Will you remember me in five years?
Yes.
Knock-Knock.
Who's there?
See! You've forgotten me already.

Who's there?
Willis.
Willis who?
Willis rain never stop?

Who's there?
Willoughby.
Willoughby who?
Willoughby a monkey's uncle!

Who's there?
Wilma.
Wilma who?
Wilma dreams come true?

Who's there?
Wooden shoe.
Wooden shoe who?
Wooden shoe like to know?

Who's there?
X.
X who?
X for breakfast.

Who's there?
Xavier.
Xavier who?
Xavier breath! I'm not leaving.

Who's there?
Xenia.
Xenia who?
Xenia stealing my joke book.

Who's there?
Zany.
Zany who?
Zany body home?

Who's there?
Zeke.
Zeke who?
''Zeke and ye shall find . . .''

Who's there?
Zinnia.
Zinnia who?
Zinnia on TV.

Who's there?
Zippy.
Zippy who?
Mrs. Zippy.

Who's there?
Zizi.
Zizi who?
Zizi when you know how.

Who's there?
Zone.
Zone who?
Zone shadow scares him.

Who's there?
Zookeeper.
Zookeeper who?
Zookeeper way from me!

Who's there?
Zoom.
Zoom who?
Zoom did you expect?

Who's there?
Yacht.
Yacht who?
Yacht 'a know me by now.

Who's there?
Yachts.
Yachts who?
Yachts up, Doc?

Who's there?
Yah.
Yah who?
Ride 'em, cowboy!

Who's there?
Yelp.
Yelp who?
Yelp me—My nose is stuck in the keyhole.

Who's there?
Yoga.
Yoga who?
Yoga what it takes!

Who's there?
Yogi Bear.
Yogi Bear who?
Yogi Bear (you go bare) and you're going to get arrested.

Who's there?
Yolanda.
Yolanda who?
Yolanda me some money?

Who's there?
You.
You who?
You who yourself!

Who's there?
Yucatan.
Yucatan who?
"Yucatan fool some of the people some of the time . . ."

Who's there?
Yukon.
Yukon who?
Yukon say that again.

Who's there?
Yvonne.
Yvonne who?
Yvonne to be alone?

Who's there?
Lettuce.
Lettuce who?
Lettuce try tomorrow.

Who's there?
Cedar.
Cedar who?
Join the Navy and Cedar world.

Who's there?
Candy.
Candy who?
Candy cow jump over the moon?

Who's there?
Orange.
Orange who?
Orange you glad I didn't say banana?

Who's there?
Zsa Zsa.
Zsa Zsa who?
Zsa Zsa last knock-knock joke I want to hear.

Why does a chicken lay an egg?
If she dropped it, it would break.

How can you drop an egg 3 feet without breaking it?
Drop it 4 feet. For the first 3 feet the egg will not hit anything.

Why is a room full of married couples empty?
Because there is not a single person in it.

What is the difference between a greedy person and an electric toaster?
One takes the most and the other makes the toast.

What man is strong enough to hold up a car with one hand?
A policeman.

Why do you always start to walk with the right foot first?
Because when you move one foot, the other one is always left behind.

When do you swallow your words?
When you eat alphabet soup.

What goes out black and comes in white?
A black cow in a snowstorm.

Is it better to write on a full or on an empty stomach?
Neither. Paper is much better.

Where do fish wash themselves?
In the river basin.

What can you add to a bucket of water that will make it weigh less?
Holes.

Where do cars get the most flat tyres?
Where there is a fork in the road.

Why is the number nine like a peacock?
Because it is nothing without its tail.

What "bus" crossed the ocean?
Columbus.

What kind of tickle doesn't make you laugh?
A tickle in your throat.

How do you make a cigarette lighter?
Take out the tobacco.

How do you make notes of stone?
Rearrange the letters.

What kind of pool can't you swim in?
A car pool.

Why are dogs like trees?
They both have barks.

What kind of umbrella does the Queen of England carry on a rainy day?
A wet one.

What kind of bird is always around when there is something to eat or drink?
A swallow.

Why don't scarecrows have any fun?
Because they are stuffed shirts.

How can you go without sleep for seven days and not be tired?
Sleep at night.

Why are identical twins like a broken alarm clock?
Because they are dead ringers.

What lands as often on its tail as it does its head?
A penny.

How many acorns grow on the average pine tree?
None. Pine trees don't have acorns.

What is always behind the times?
The back of a clock.

What goes through a door but never goes in or out?
A keyhole.

What can turn without moving?
Milk. It can turn sour.

What code message is the same from left to right, right to left, upside down and right side up?
S.O.S.

Why does the stork stand on one leg only?
If he lifted it, he would fall down.

How is a pig like a horse?
When a pig is hungry he eats like a horse, and when a horse is hungry he eats like a pig.

On which side does a chicken have the most feathers?
On the outside.

Why do you say that whales talk a lot?
Because they are always spouting off.

What invention allows you to see through walls?
A window.

What has two legs like an Indian, two eyes like an Indian, two hands like an Indian, looks just like an Indian — but is not an Indian?
The picture of an Indian.

What is the difference between a banana and a bell?
You can only peel (peal) the banana once.

What can a whole apple do that half an apple can't do?
It can look round.

When is a man not a man?
When he turns into an alley.

If April showers bring May flowers, what do the Mayflowers bring?
Pilgrims.

What baby is born with whiskers?
A kitten.

How should you treat a baby goat?
Like a kid.

What kind of coat has no sleeves, no buttons, no pockets and won't keep you warm?
A coat of paint.

What kind of fall makes you unconscious but doesn't hurt you?
Falling asleep.

What turns everything around but doesn't move?
A mirror.

What was the largest island in the world before Australia was discovered?
Australia.

How do we know Rome was built at night?
Because Rome wasn't built in a day.

What lives in winter, dies in summer, and grows with its roots upwards?
An icicle.

Why do hummingbirds hum?
Because they can't read music.

What kind of pliers do you use in arithmetic?
Multipliers.

What is locomotion?
A crazy dance.

If you had 5 potatoes and had to divide them equally between 3 people, what should you do?
Mash them first.

What do they do with a tree after they chop it down?
Chop it up.

When are eyes not eyes?
When the wind makes them water.

What is ploughed but never planted?
Snow.

What did Columbus see on his right hand when he discovered America?
Five fingers.

How can you make a fire with only one stick?
Easy. Just make sure it's a matchstick.

Why is the letter B hot?
Because it makes oil boil.

What has four fingers and a thumb but is not a hand?
A glove.

What has a hundred limbs but can't walk?
A tree.

What is the longest word in the world?
Rubber, because it stretches.

How much dirt is there in a hole exactly one foot deep and one foot across?
None. A hole is empty.

When will a net hold water?
When the water is frozen into ice.

How are 2 plus 2 equal 5 and your left hand alike?
Neither is right.

What goes further the slower it goes?
Money.

What kind of bow can't be tied?
A rainbow.

Why doesn't it cost much to feed a horse?
Because a horse eats best when it doesn't have a bit in its mouth.

How many worms make a foot?
Twelve inch worms.

How many feet are in a yard?
It depends on how many people are standing in it.

What has a foot on each side and one in the middle?
A yardstick.

How do we know that mountain goats have feet?
Because they are sure-footed.

Why can't it rain for two nights in a row?
Because there is a day between.

What colour is rain?
Water colour.

What goes through water but doesn't get wet?
A ray of light.

What is a small cad?
A caddy.

What has a neck but no head?
A bottle.

Why is your nose in the middle of your face?
Because it is the scenter (centre).

If an egg came floating down the River Thames, where did it come from?
From a chicken.

What can you put in a glass but never take out of it?
A crack.

Why do elephants have trunks?
Because they don't have pockets to put things in.

Why does the giraffe have a long neck?
Because his head is so far from his body.

Why is a pig in the house like a house on fire?
Because the sooner you put it out, the better.

What goes from side to side, and up and down, but never moves?
A road.

What is a dark horse?
A nightmare.

Why shouldn't you keep a library book on the ground overnight?
Because in the morning it will be overdue (dew).

What is on your arm and in the sea?
A muscle (mussel).

Every morning the farmer had eggs for breakfast. He owned no chickens and he never got eggs from anyone else's chickens. Where did he get the eggs?
From his ducks.

What animals follow everywhere you go?
Your calves.

What do elephants have that no other animals have?
Baby elephants.

What is shaped like a box, has no feet and runs up and down?
A lift.

What is pointed in one direction and headed in the other?
A pin.

What can you hold in your left hand but not in your right hand?
Your right elbow.

What is in the middle of March?
The letter R.

What kind of car drives over water?
Any kind of car, if it goes over a bridge.

What is the difference between a truthful person and a liar?
One lies when he sleeps, the other lies all the time.

Two men dig a hole in five days. How many days would it take them to dig half a hole?
None. You can't dig half a hole.

What is dark but made by light?
A shadow.

How can you place a pencil on the floor so that no one can jump over it?
Put it next to the wall.

What increases its value by being turned upside down?
The number 6.

What do you lose every time you stand up?
Your lap.

When is a black dog not a black dog?
When it is a greyhound.

Where do children grow?
In a kindergarten.

How is a burning candle like thirst?
A bit of water ends both of them.

Why is it so easy to weigh fish?
Because the fish have their own scales.

How many sides does a box have?
Two, the inside and the outside.

When can a man be 6 feet tall and short at the same time?
When he is short of money.

What is the centre of gravity?
The letter V.

Is it better to say, "The yolk of an egg is white," or "The yolk of an egg are white?"
Neither. An egg yolk is yellow.

Why should a man's hair turn grey before his moustache?
Because it is older.

What kind of beans won't grow in a garden?
Jelly beans.

When do you go as fast as a racing car?
When you are in it.

What is the difference between a racer and a locomotive engineer?
One is trained to run, the other runs a train.

From what number can you take half and leave nothing?
The number is 8. Take away the top half and o is left.

Which is more nourishing, a cow or a shooting star?
A shooting star, because it is meteor (meatier).

What is never out of sight?
The letter S.

What happens if you talk when there is food in your mouth?
You will have said a mouthful.

What does grass say when it is cut?
"I don't mow (know)."